PIXAR

SiMPLY COLOURING

AUTUMN PUBLISHING

The start of
something special

Ready for a new day

The Incredibles

Barley and Ian

Welcome!

The toys are back in town!

A bright future

Young Dory loves to explore

The best of friends

Only the yummiest food will do

Time for tea

Watch out!

The start of a new quest

Hang on!

Training time!

Elastigirl saves the day!

Anger is
never happy

Ready to race!

Wall•E sees something interesting

The best chef in town

Miguel and Dante

Champions!

Jack-Jack is
coming, too!

Hank and Dory

Howling in the moonlight

A storm is coming!

An incredible family

Marlin has a new friend

Burning rubber!

The Emotions are a great team

A new generation